DOODLEBOB

Popcorn
ELT
Readers

This is a magic pencil. It draws pictures. The pictures move and live.

This is **DoodleBob**. He's a drawing and he's dangerous!

This is **Squidward**. He's an octopus. He doesn't always like SpongeBob and Patrick.

Before you read ...
What do you think? What does SpongeBob draw with the magic pencil?

3

New Words

What do these new words mean?
 Ask your teacher or use your dictionary.

drop

He **dropped** the ball.

artist

She's an **artist**.

erase

She's **erasing** the number.

drawing

This is a **drawing** of a cat.

fight

They are **fighting**.

hole

He's looking into a **hole**.

hurt

Her foot **hurts**.

magic

This is a magician.
He does **magic**.

pencil

This is a **pencil**.

swim

She is **swimming**.

'I've got an idea.'

Verbs

Present	Past
draw	drew
swim	swam
fall	fell

CHAPTER ONE
The magic pencil

One day an artist was at sea. He started drawing. Then he dropped his pencil.

'No!' he shouted. 'My pencil is in the water! Now I can't draw.'

Down in Bikini Bottom, SpongeBob was with his friend Patrick. The two friends played together happily.

Suddenly something big dropped next to them. They were very frightened.

'What's that, SpongeBob?' asked Patrick.

'I think it's a big pencil,' said SpongeBob.

'Go and look!' said Patrick. 'I'm going to stay here behind the house.'

SpongeBob looked at it.

'Yes, it's a very big pencil,' he said. 'Let's draw some pictures.'

'What are you going to draw?' asked Patrick.

SpongeBob drew a picture and Patrick looked at the picture.

'That's good, SpongeBob. Oh look! Your drawing is moving!' he said.

'Patrick,' said SpongeBob. 'I think it's a *magic* pencil!'

'Wow! A magic pencil,' said Patrick. 'Draw some hair on me.'

SpongeBob drew some hair on Patrick. The two friends laughed.

'Oh look,' said Patrick. 'The hair is swimming away. Yes, it is magic!'

Squidward was in his house.

'I'm handsome,' thought Squidward, 'but I don't have any hair.'

Suddenly the magic hair swam into Squidward's house. It stopped on Squidward's head. Squidward was very happy.

'I've got hair,' he said. 'Now I'm very handsome!'

'I'm going to draw something now,' said Patrick. Then he drew a face with the magic pencil.

'What's that?' asked SpongeBob.

'It's Squidward!' said Patrick. The drawing of Squidward started to move. It made noises.

'It's horrible!' said SpongeBob. He quickly erased the drawing.

'I've got an idea,' said SpongeBob. 'Let's go to Squidward's house.'

At Squidward's house SpongeBob drew some money outside the door. Then he went behind the house with Patrick. 'This is going to be funny!' he said.

'Hello Squidward!' SpongeBob shouted. 'Are you at home?'

Squidward opened the door and saw the money.

'Watch this!' said SpongeBob to Patrick.

'What's this? Money!' said Squidward. But suddenly the money moved.

'Oh no!' he said.

Then Squidward's new hair swam away.

'Oh no! My hair!'

SpongeBob and Patrick laughed. Squidward was angry.

'It was you!' he said. He went back into his house and closed the door.

CHAPTER TWO
DoodleBob

'I've got an idea,' said SpongeBob. 'I'm going to draw a *DoodleBob*! A picture of me!'

He drew the picture and it moved.

'Look!' said Patrick. 'DoodleBob is walking away! He's talking to Squidward!'

'Oh no!' said SpongeBob. 'Now he's hurting Squidward. Stop, DoodleBob!'

DoodleBob ran back to SpongeBob. Suddenly he had the magic pencil in his hands! He was very fast and very strong. SpongeBob and Patrick fell down.

'Oh no!' said SpongeBob. 'Now DoodleBob has the magic pencil!'

'He's running away,' said Patrick. 'He's drawing a house. Now he's inside it.'

'Let's go,' said SpongeBob.

'No,' said Patrick. 'I'm not going in there.'

'It's OK,' said SpongeBob. 'I'm behind you.'

SpongeBob and Patrick walked slowly to the house.

'It's not far now,' said SpongeBob. But DoodleBob drew a big hole in front of his house. The two friends fell into the hole.

'Oh no!' they shouted.

'DoodleBob is dangerous,' said SpongeBob. 'We must stop him!'

SpongeBob and Patrick watched DoodleBob. He ran around noisily with the pencil. He looked very dangerous. After a long time he put the pencil down.

The two friends jumped on DoodleBob.

'I've got the pencil,' said SpongeBob. 'Now I'm going to erase you!'

SpongeBob erased DoodleBob.

'We did it! We stopped him!' said SpongeBob.

The friends walked away happily. They didn't see DoodleBob's hand moving behind them ...

CHAPTER THREE
A fight in the night

'That was a very exciting day,' thought SpongeBob, 'but I'm going to bed now. Goodnight magic pencil,' he said. Then SpongeBob went to sleep.

In the night DoodleBob's hand came into SpongeBob's house. It came into SpongeBob's room. The hand found the magic pencil. Then it drew DoodleBob's arms, legs and head again.

Suddenly SpongeBob saw DoodleBob. He was very frightened.

'DoodleBob! You're back! Are you angry with me?' he asked.

'*You* are a *drawing*! *I* am *SpongeBob*!' shouted DoodleBob.

'Aaaarrr!' said SpongeBob and he ran away. DoodleBob ran after SpongeBob with the magic pencil. He erased SpongeBob's eye, arm and leg!

'Oh no!' said SpongeBob. 'Give me that pencil, DoodleBob!'

SpongeBob and DoodleBob started fighting for the pencil. It was a fast and noisy fight, but now SpongeBob had the pencil.

Quickly, he drew his eye, arm and leg again.

'I'm going to fight you now, DoodleBob,' said SpongeBob, 'and I'm going to win!'

But SpongeBob dropped the pencil ...

'Oh no!' thought SpongeBob. 'What am I going to do now? DoodleBob is going to erase me!'

But DoodleBob put his foot on some paper and ... he *stopped*!

'He can't move!' thought SpongeBob. 'He can't move his foot off the paper because he's a drawing!'

SpongeBob saw a big book.

'I've got an idea,' he thought. 'I'm going to put DoodleBob inside the book.'

Very quickly, he closed the big book on DoodleBob. Bang!

SpongeBob opened the book. He saw DoodleBob inside it. He wasn't moving. He was a drawing again!

'Are you OK, SpongeBob?' shouted Patrick outside the door. He ran into SpongeBob's house. 'There was a lot of noise.'

'I'm OK,' said SpongeBob. 'Look at this!'

Patrick looked at the drawing.

'Oh no, it's DoodleBob!' he said.

'Yes, but he's happy because he's on paper,' said SpongeBob. 'He's not dangerous now.'

'The magic in the pencil is dangerous,' said SpongeBob. 'It must go.'

'OK,' said Patrick. 'Let's throw it far away.'

'Goodbye magic pencil!' they shouted.

The artist on the sea saw something fly out of the water.

'It's my pencil!' he shouted. 'I can finish my drawing now.'

THE END

OCTOPUSES AND SEA STARS

In Bikini Bottom, Squidward is an octopus and Patrick is a sea star. Let's read about real octopuses and sea stars ...

CLEVER OCTOPUSES

* They can see very well.
* They can swim very fast.
* They can change colour.
* They can go into very small holes.
* When they are frightened they squirt ink and they swim away.
* They have eight arms. If they lose an arm they can make one again.
* They have three hearts.

BEAUTIFUL SEA STARS

✱ They can be a lot of different colours.

✱ They do not swim. They walk very slowly.

✱ A lot of sea stars have five arms but some have many more – sometimes fifty!

✱ Sea stars can make an arm again if they lose one.

Did you know ...?

Sea stars' eyes are at the end of their arms!

Do you know any other interesting sea animals?

What do these words mean? Find out.

change   squirt   ink
lose   heart

After you read

1 Match the halves of the sentences.

a) The artist shouted 'No!'

b) SpongeBob said 'It's a magic pencil'

c) SpongeBob erased DoodleBob

d) Squidward was angry

e) DoodleBob stopped

i) because his foot was on some paper.

ii) because the money and the hair swam away.

iii) because he dropped his pencil.

iv) because the drawing moved.

v) because he was dangerous.

2 Answer the questions.

a) Who dropped the pencil in the sea?   the artist

b) Who drew Squidward?   ....

c) Who drew some hair?   ....

d) Who said 'I'm very handsome!'?   ....

e) Who drew a hole?   ....

f) What was magic?   ....

Where's the popcorn?
Look in your book.
Can you find it?

Puzzle time!

1 What is in picture A but not in picture B? Circle
   five things and write the words.

a) ___hair___   b) _____   c) _____
d) _____   e) _____   f) _____

2 Find four more past tense verbs from the story in
  the pencil. Draw a circle around them. Then find
  the words in your book.

drew droppedfellswamerased

29

3 Label the picture. Use the words in the box.

~~eye~~   hand   leg   arm   foot   face

a
..... eye .....

b
....

c
....

d
....

e
....

f
....

4 Draw a character from the story. Write a description.

Name: This is ....

Animal: He is a ....

Colour: He is ....

Imagine...

Work in pairs. Play 'Pictionary' in English!
For example:

What are you going to draw?

Watch me. You can guess.

Is it Squidward?

Yes it is!

1 🅣7 **Listen and read.**

Go away, DoodleBob!

An artist drops his pencil,
It falls into the sea.
SpongeBob says, 'It's magic!
I can draw a magic me!'

SpongeBob draws his picture,
But DoodleBob is bad.
He takes the magic pencil
And everyone is sad.

'DoodleBob, you're dangerous,'
Says SpongeBob. 'Go away!'
He puts DoodleBob on paper
And everything's OK!
Yes! Everything's OK!

2 🅣8 **Say the chant.**